S0-ABT-625

Crayola

Bug Buddies

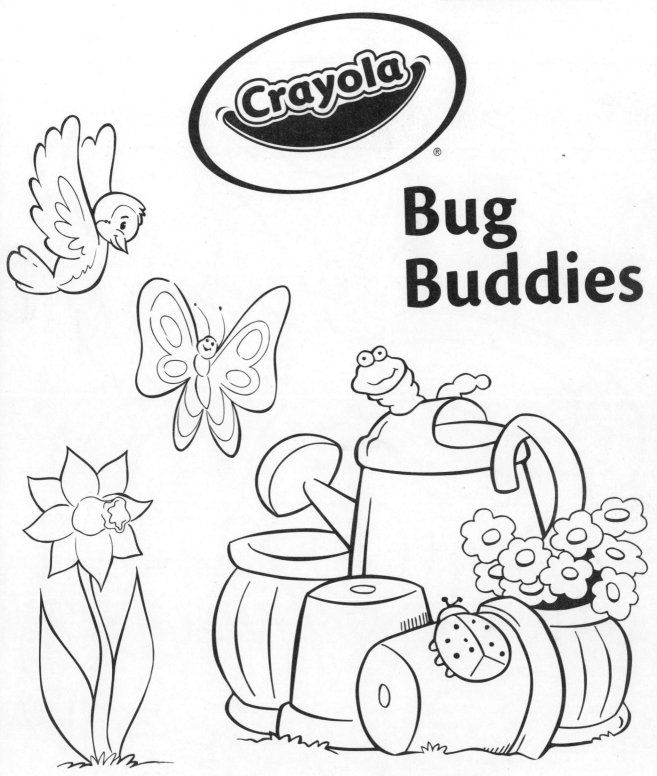

Dalmatian Press, LLC 2012. All rights reserved. Printed in the U.S.A.
The DALMATIAN PRESS name, logo, and Tear and Share are trademarks of Dalmatian Publishing Group, Franklin, Tennessee 37067. 1-866-418-2572. No part of this book may be reproduced or copied in any form without written permission from the copyright owner. Art © 2012 DPG.

Dalmatian Press

12 13 14 15 NGS 37873 10 9 8 7 6 5 4
19429 Crayola Way Big Book to Color — Bug Buddies

Which one is different?

A

B

C

D

E

Your Answer

Answer: D

Trace and color!

THE BIRDS

How many bees do you count?

Answer: 15

Your Answer

Which one does not belong?

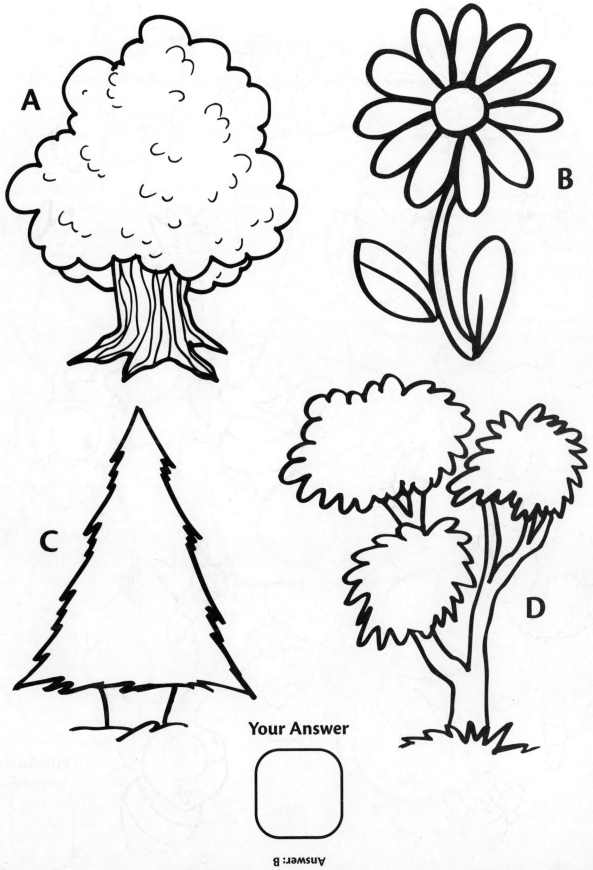

A

B

C

D

Your Answer

Color the lines that lead from each egg.
Which one leads to the chicken?

A   B   C

Your Answer

USE YOUR IMAGINATION!

Draw what is growing in the pot.

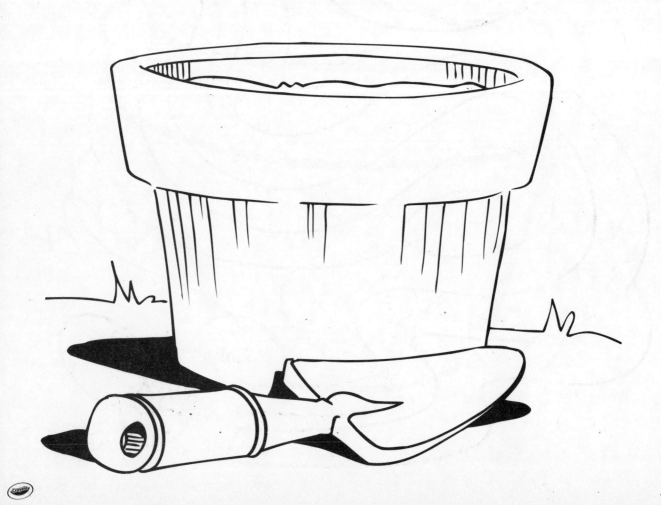

Help the chicken get back to the egg.

Start

Finish

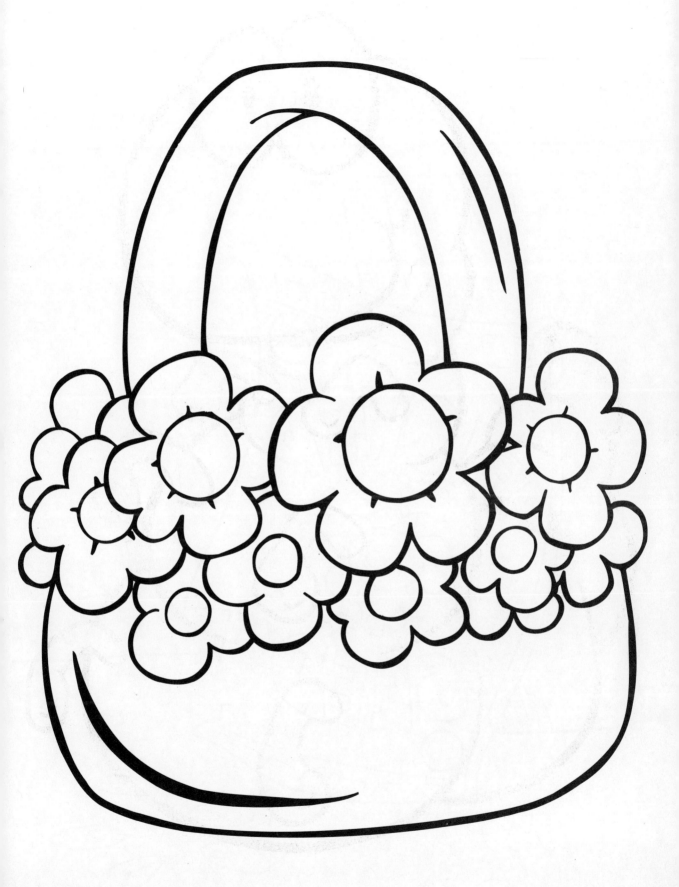

FLOWER SEEDS

5¢

5¢

22

24

Which one does not belong?

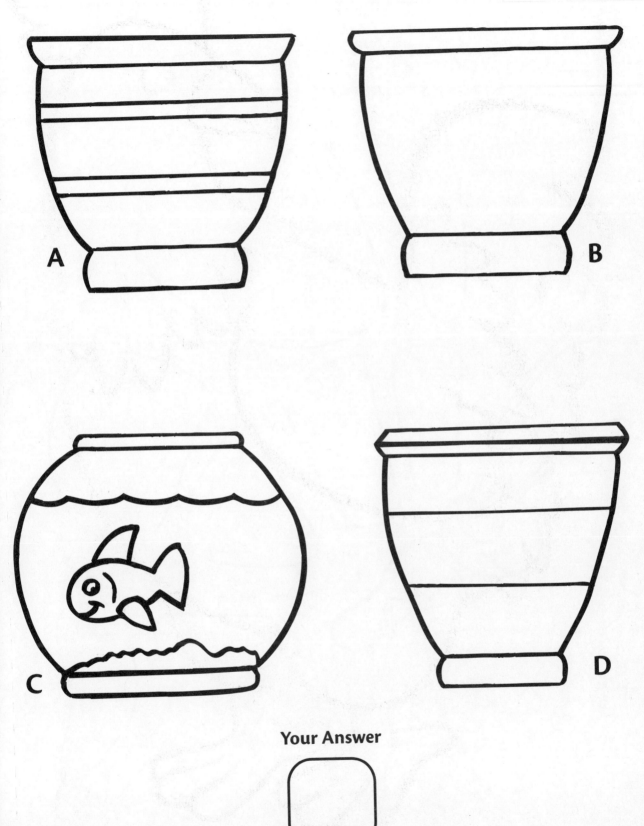

A

B

C

D

Your Answer

Dalmatian Press

Trace and color!

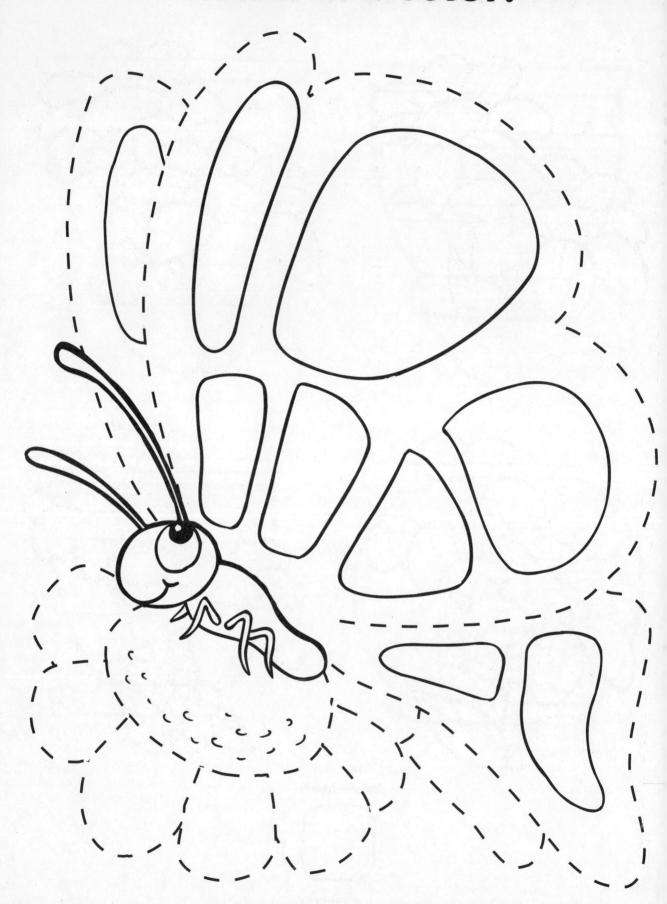

Which one is different?

Your Answer

Color by number.

1. Yellow   2. Orange   3. Green   4. Brown

Which one does not belong?

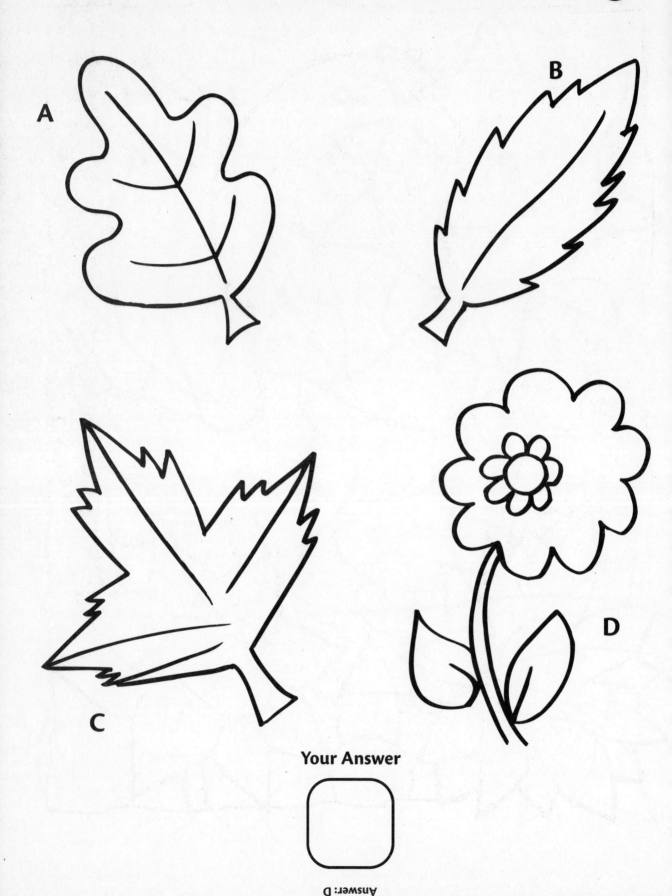

A

B

C

D

Your Answer

Which one does not belong?

A

B

C

D

Your Answer

34

Find your way through the maze.

Finish

Start

Color by number.

1. Red   2. Yellow   3. Yellow Green
4. Green   5. Blue   6. Orange   7. Brown

38

Trace and color!

Which one does not belong?

A

B

C

D

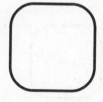

44

Which one is different?

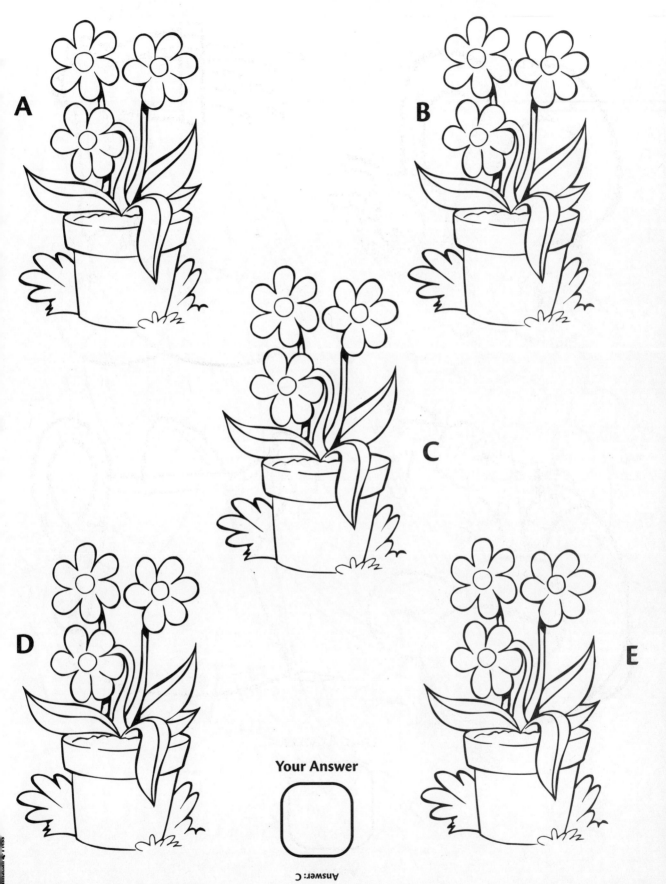

A

B

C

D

E

Your Answer

Answer: C

Connect the dots—and color!

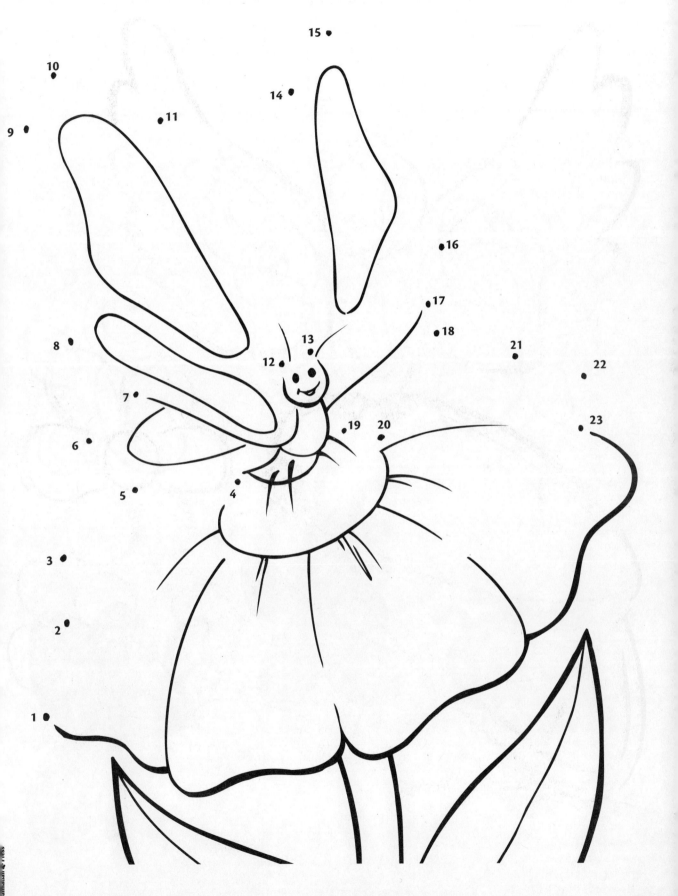

Draw a line from each butterfly to its matching shadow.

How many apples do you count?

Your Answer

Connect the dots—and color!

Connect the dots—and color!

Which one is different?

A

B

C

D

E

Your Answer

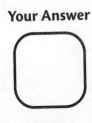

Dalmatian Press

Finish drawing the picture of the basket of flowers.

Trace and color!

CARROT

Which one is different?

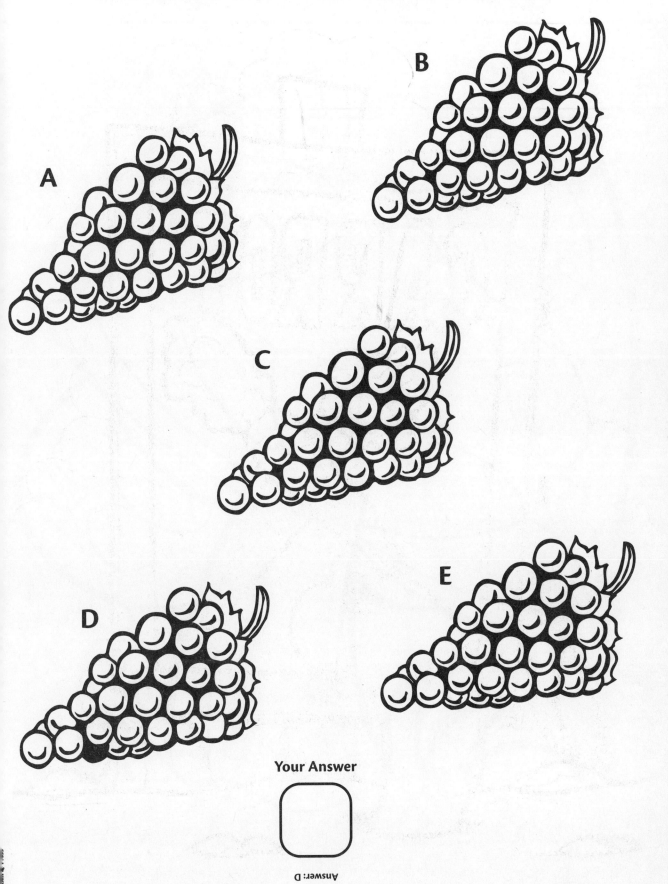

Your Answer

Connect the dots—and color!

How many birds and butterflies do you count?

Your Answer

Crayola

Color the lines that lead from the baby birds. Which one leads to the nest?

Your Answer

Answer: C

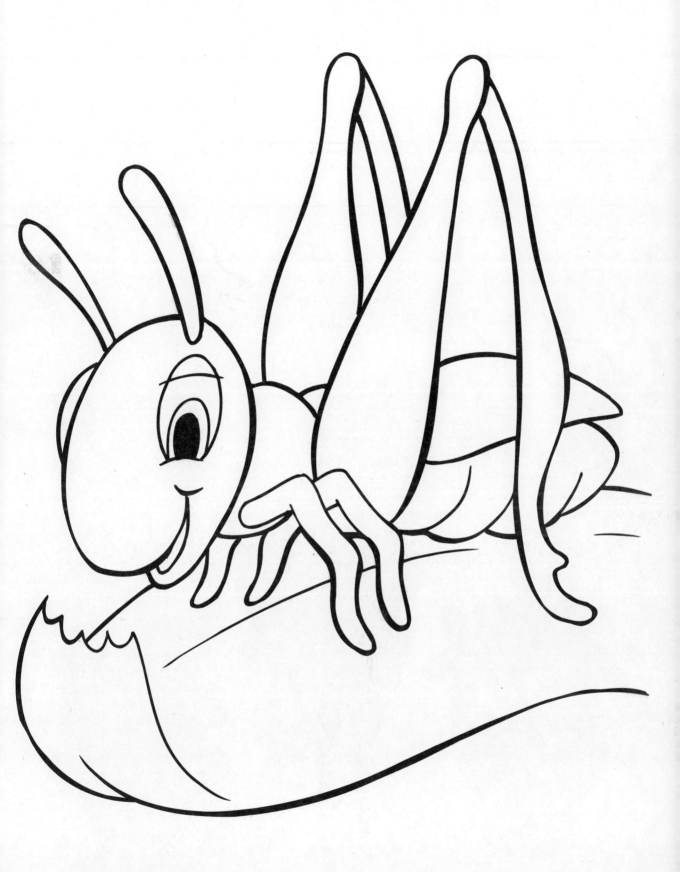

Draw a line from each flower pot to its matching shadow.

98

Trace and color!

Dalmatian ❦ Press

Color by number.

**1. Red   2. Yellow   3. Yellow Orange   4. Green
5. Blue   6. Orange   7. Violet   8. Blue Violet**

Connect the dots—and color!

Which one does not belong?

A

B

C

D

Your Answer

Answer: D

11

Which one does not belong?

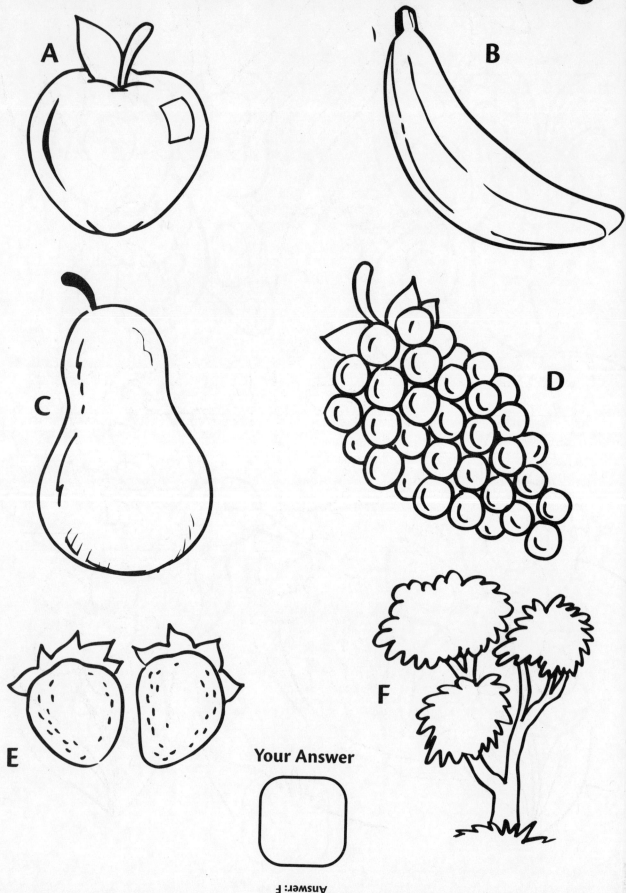

A

B

C

D

E

F

Your Answer

Answer: F

11

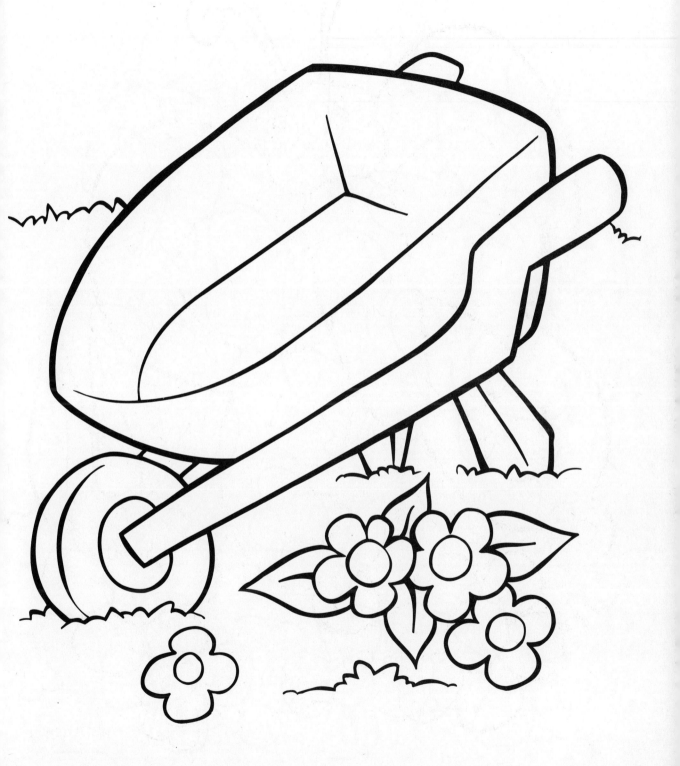

How many butterflies do you count?

Your Answer

116

Which one is different?

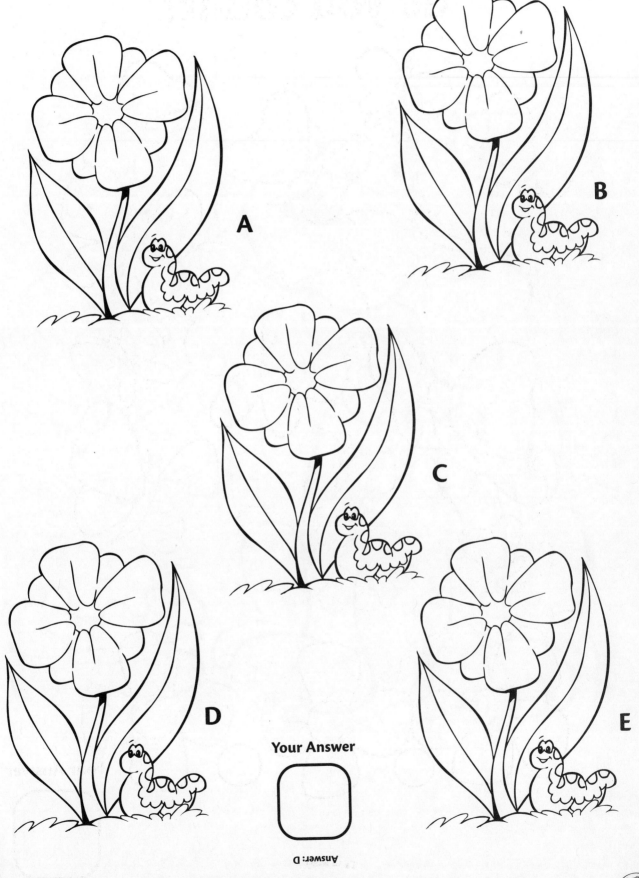

A

B

C

D

E

Your Answer

Answer: D

118

Finish drawing the picture of the butterfly.

Color the lines that lead from each bee.
Which one leads to the hive?

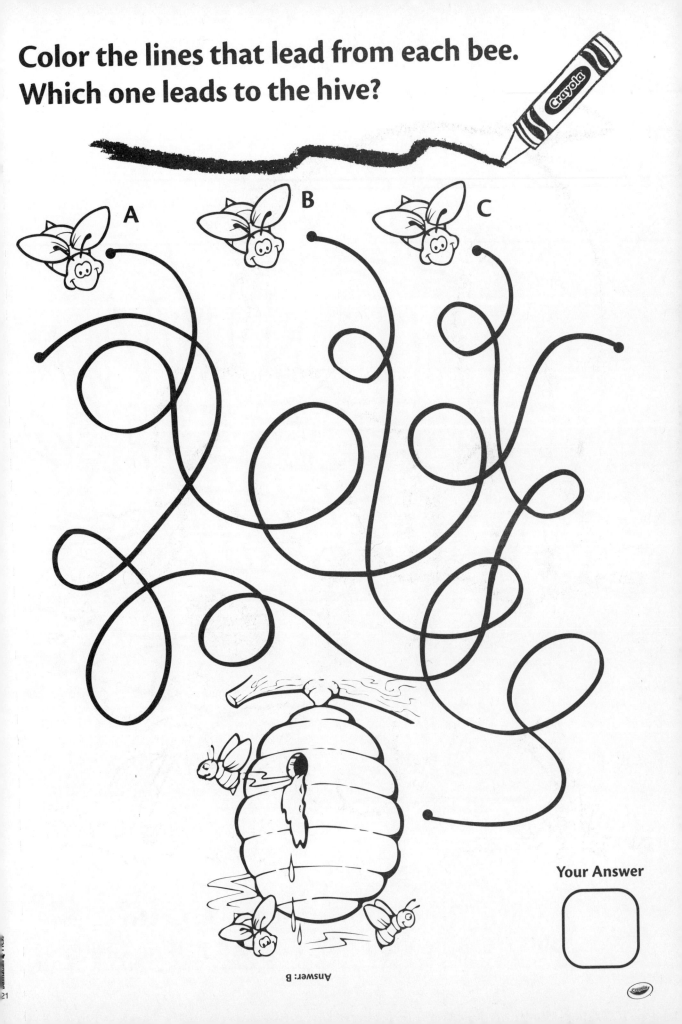

A B C

Your Answer

Answer: B

Color by number.

1. Red   **2. Yellow**   **3. Orange**   **4. Green**
5. Blue   **6. Blue Violet**   **7. Brown**   **8. Blue Green**

Draw a line from each apple to its matching shadow.

Answer: A-3; B-1; C-2

Dalmatian Press

Which one is different?

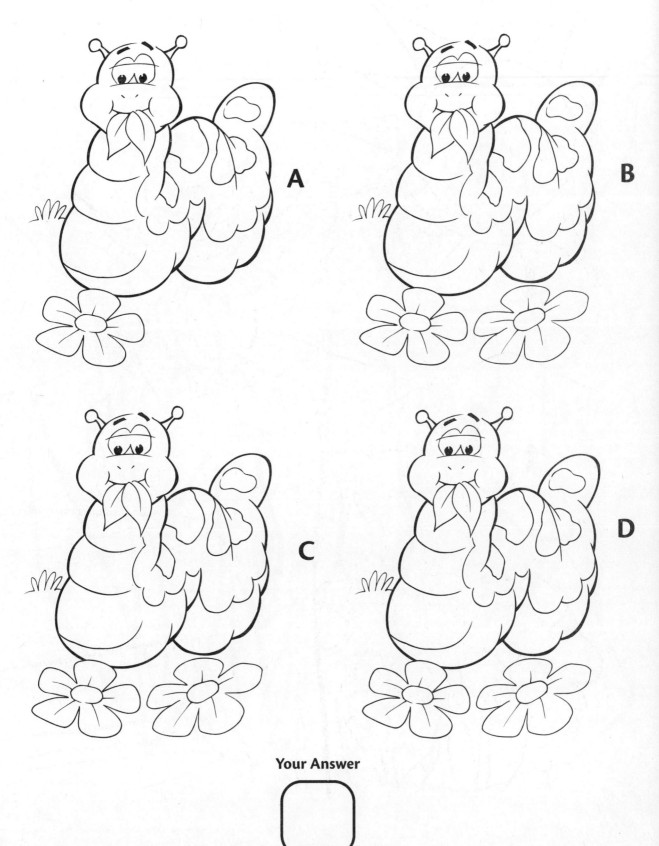

A

B

C

D

Your Answer

Answer: A

Connect the dots—and color!

Dalmatian Press

134

Find your way through the maze.

Start

Finish

Dalmatian Press

Which one is different?

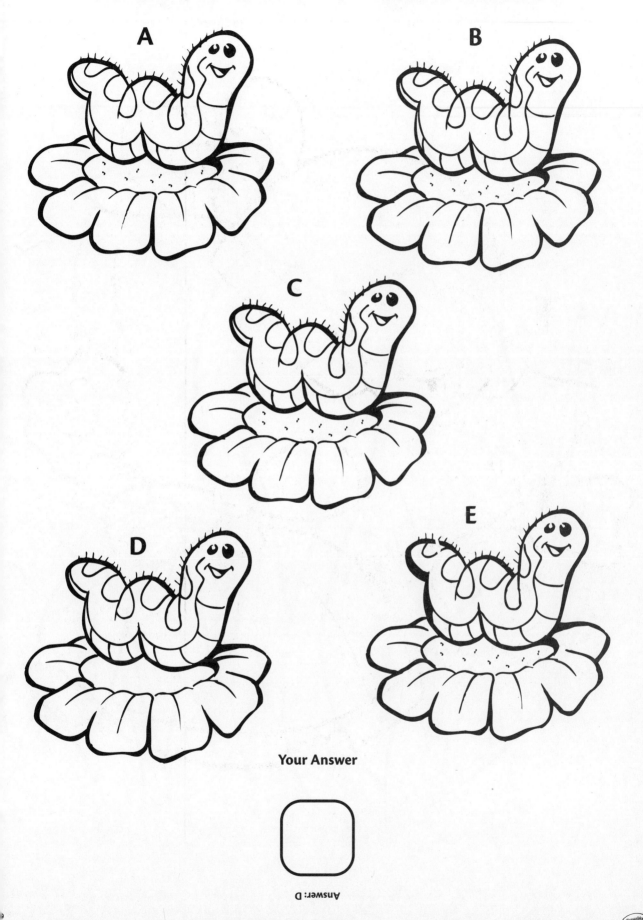

A

B

C

D

E

Your Answer

Answer: D

Art © 2011 DPG, LLC.

19429 Crayola Way Big Book to Color with Stickers

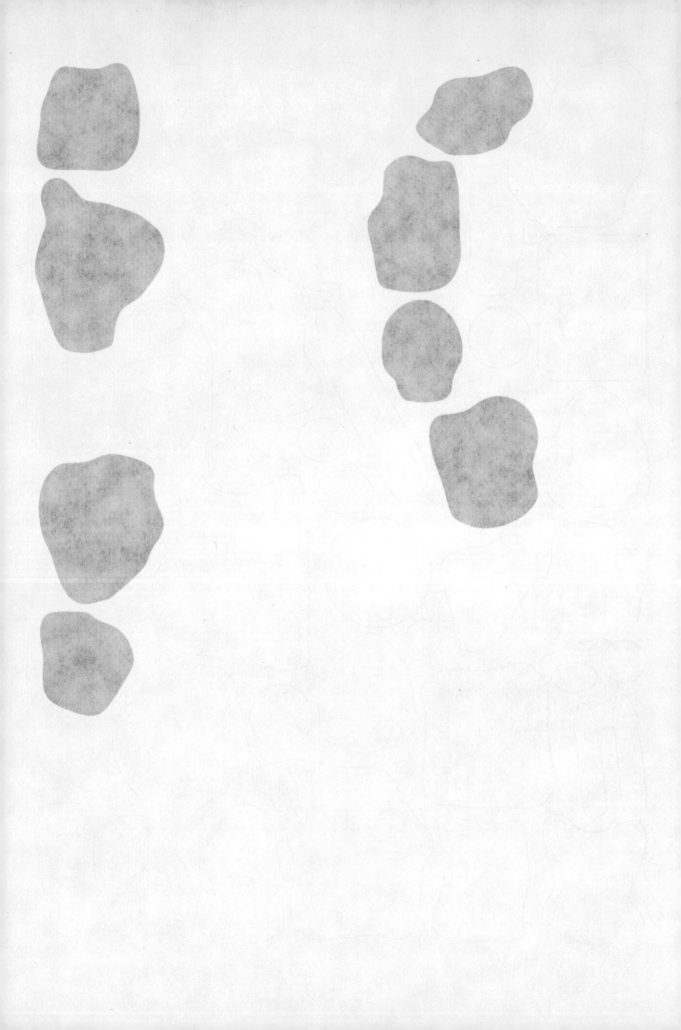

Help Horton find his way home.

Start

Finish

150

Trace and color!

15

Which one does not belong?

A

B

C

D

Your Answer

Help Suzie and Sally find their friend.

Start

Finish

How many trees do you count?

Your Answer

Connect the dots—and color!

Draw a line from each flower to its matching shadow.

172

Connect the dots—and color!

How many acorns do you count?

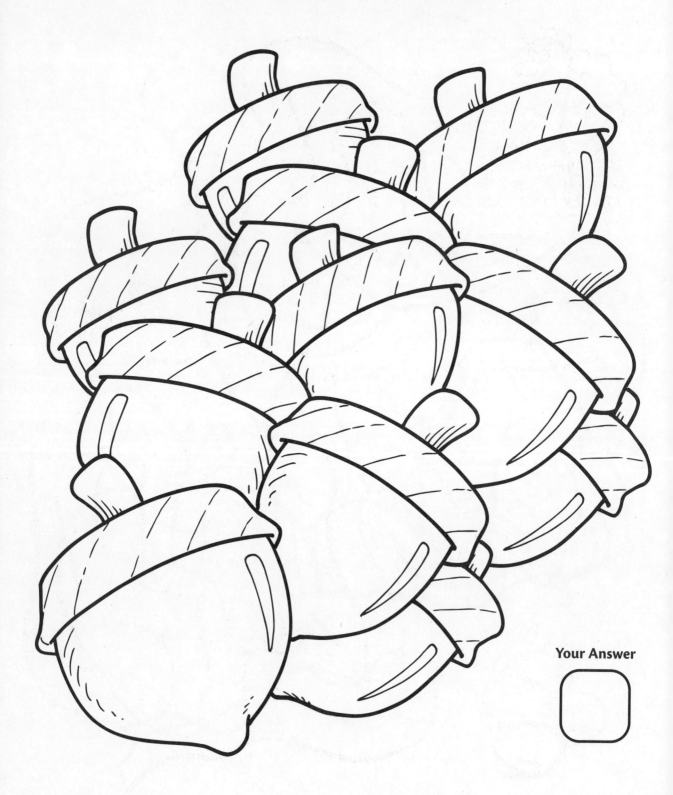

Your Answer

Help the chicken get to her eggs.

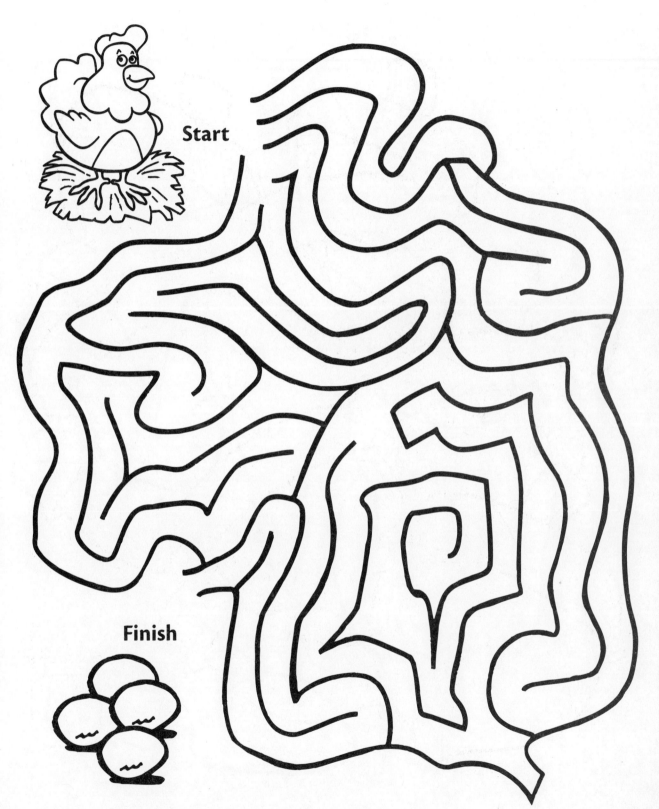

Start

Finish

Trace and color!

How many fruit bunches do you count?

Your Answer

USE YOUR IMAGINATION!

Draw a bee on the flower.

186

Which one is different?

A

B

C

D

Your Answer

Answer: C

Dalmatian Press

How many acorns and leaves do you count?

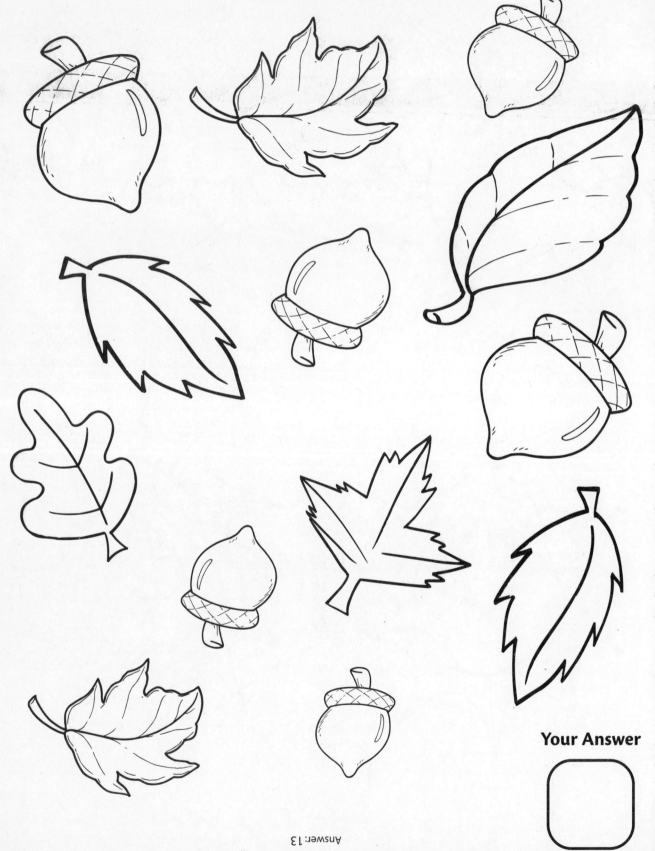

Answer: 13

Your Answer

USE YOUR IMAGINATION!

Draw yourself chasing butterflies.

Trace and color!

196

USE YOUR IMAGINATION!

Draw some buzzzy bugs!

Draw a line from each object to its matching shadow.

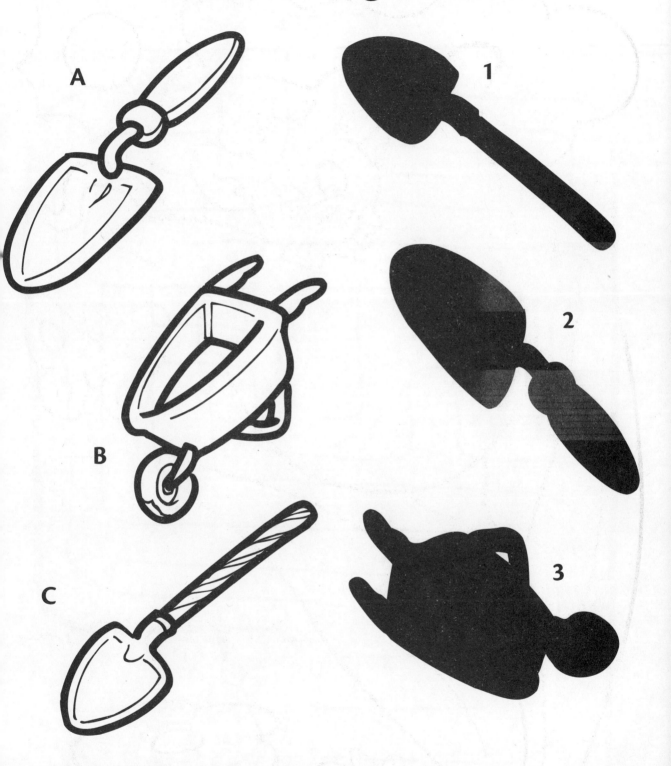

A

B

C

1

2

3

Help Bobby find his way out.

Finish

Start

Trace the line that leads from each apple. Which one leads to the tree?

A   B   C

Your Answer

Find your way through the maze.

Start

Finish

Which one is different?

A

B

C

D

Your Answer

Color by number.

1. Red   2. Yellow   3. Blue   4. Green   5. Orange

210

Draw a line from each flower to its matching shadow.

A

B

C

1

2

3

Dalmatian Press

Which one does not belong?

A

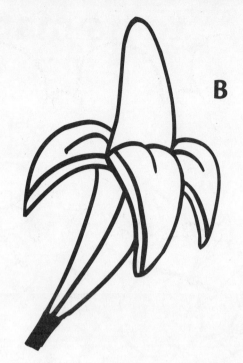

B

C

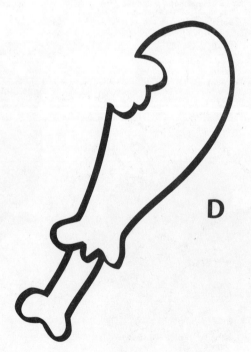

D

Your Answer

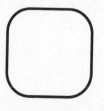

Answer: D

Trace and color!

How many grape bunches do you count?

Your Answer

Color by number.

1. Red   2. Yellow   3. Blue   4. Green   5. Orange

221

Which one is different?

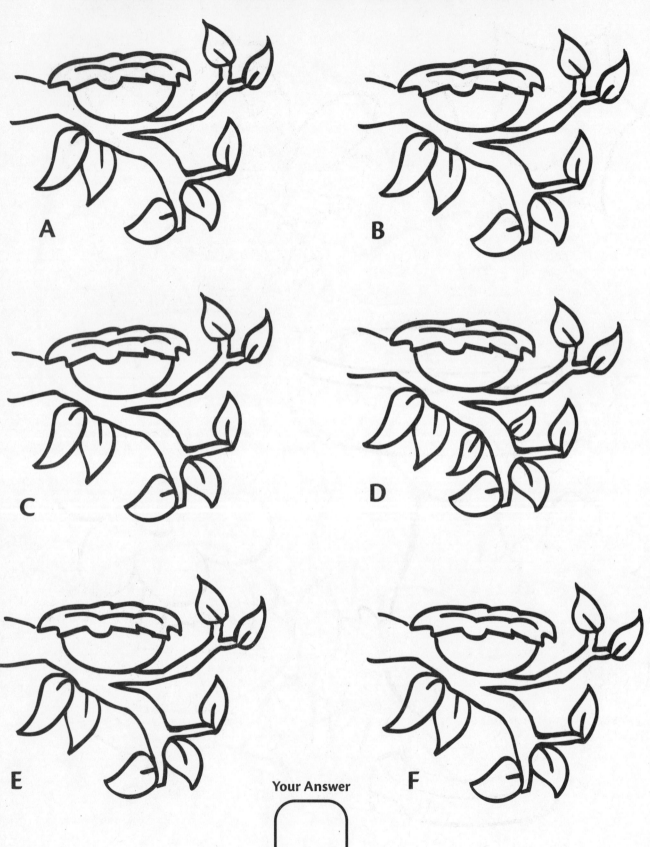

A

B

C

D

E

F

Your Answer

222

Connect the dots—and color!

USE YOUR IMAGINATION!

What animal would you like to be for a day?

Find your way through the maze.

Start

Finish

Draw a line from each fruit to its matching shadow.

Answer: A-3; B-1; C-2

230

232

Finish drawing the mushroom.

USE YOUR IMAGINATION!

What does a butterfly dream about?

Trace and color!

Draw a line from each butterfly to its matching shadow.

Color by number.

1. Yellow   2. Yellow Orange   3. Green
4. Yellow Green   5. Blue

How many carrots
do you count?

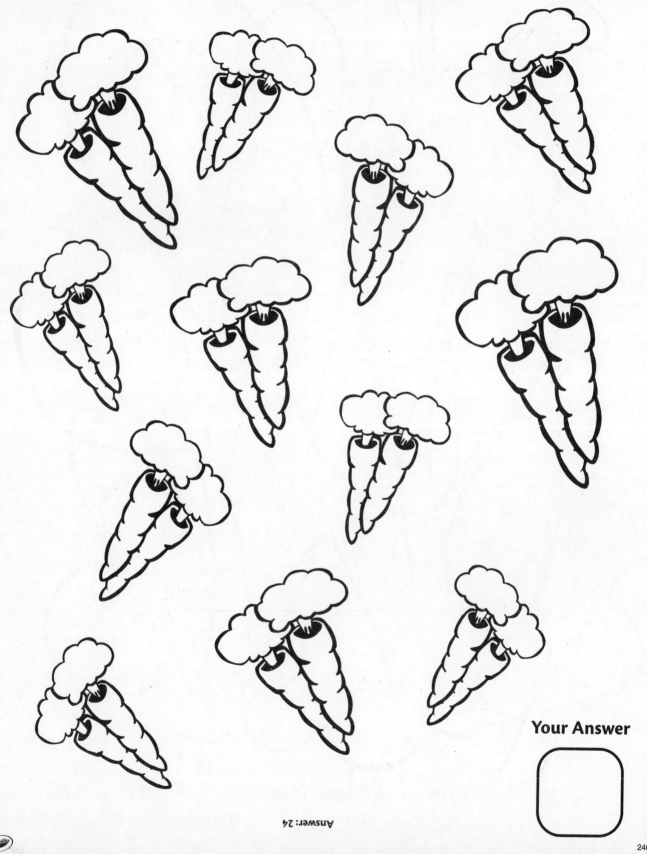

Your Answer

Which one is different?

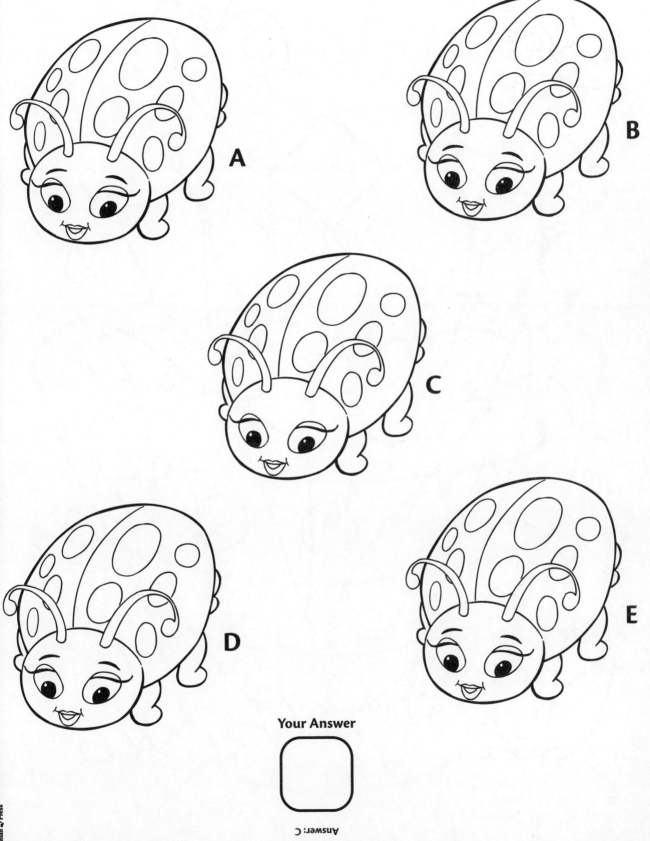

A

B

C

D

E

Your Answer

Answer: C

Color by number.

1. Red   2. Orange   3. Yellow   4. Green
5. Blue   6. Violet   7. Brown   8. Black

Draw a line from each vegetable to its matching shadow.

Trace the line that leads from each worm. Which one leads to the flower?

Your Answer

Trace and color!

Dalmatian Press

Connect the dots—and color!

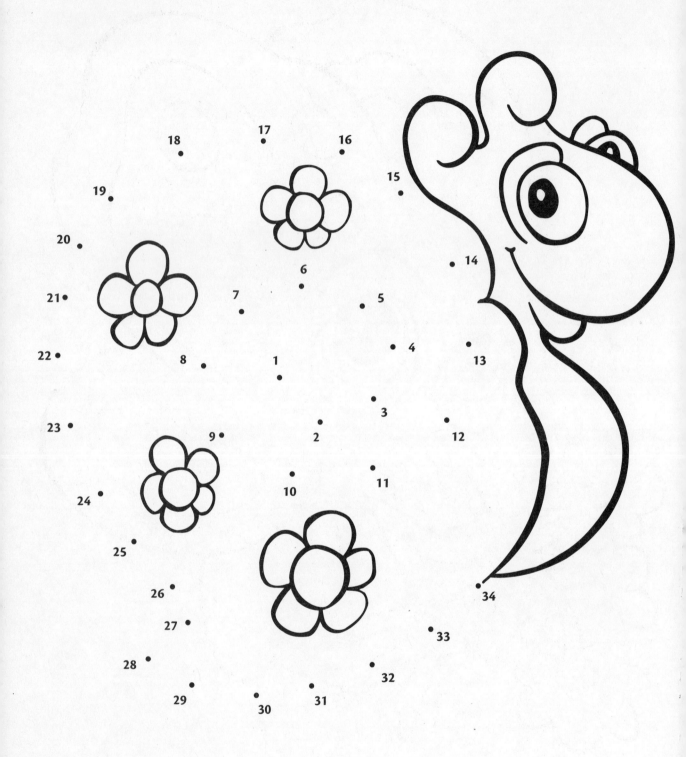

258

Color by number.

1. Yellow   2. Red   3. Blue
4. Orange   5. Green   6. Violet

261

Trace and color!

Which one does not belong?

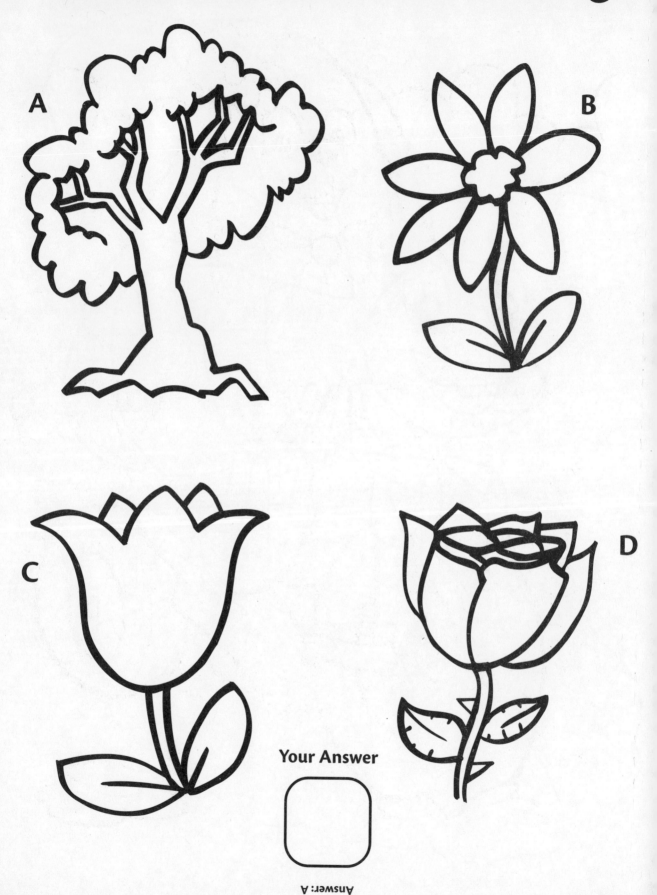

A

B

C

D

Your Answer

Answer: A

Dalmatian Press

Draw a line from each flower to its matching shadow.

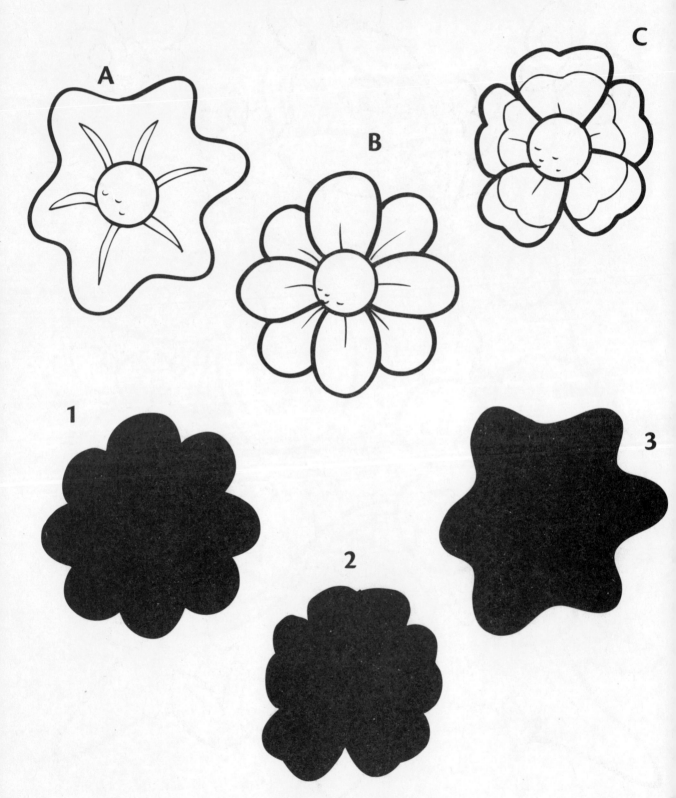

27

USE YOUR IMAGINATION!

Draw and color a pretty garden.

Connect the dots—and color!
Then draw some bees in the air.

Finish drawing the butterfly.

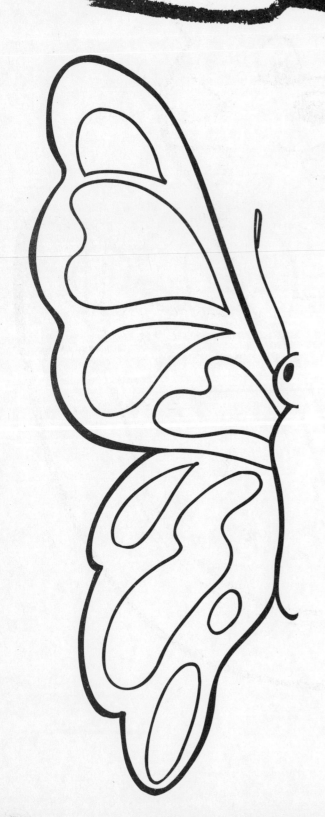

278

280

Color by number.

1. Yellow **2.** Orange **3.** Red **4.** Blue **5.** Violet
6. Green **7.** Yellow Orange **8.** Gray **9.** Brown

Trace and color!

Dalmatian Press

Draw a line from each leaf to its matching shadow.

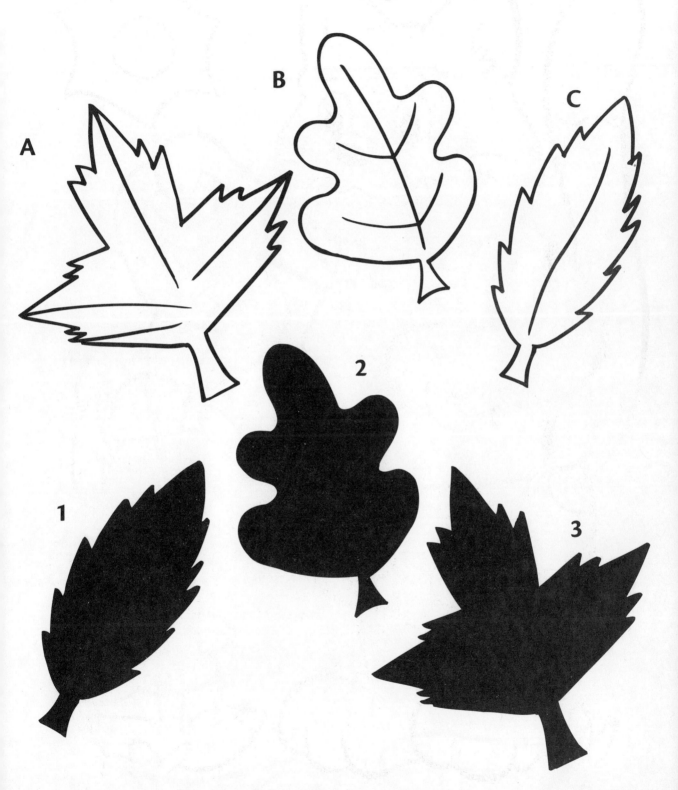

A

B

C

1

2

3

Dalmatian Press

Connect the dots—and color!

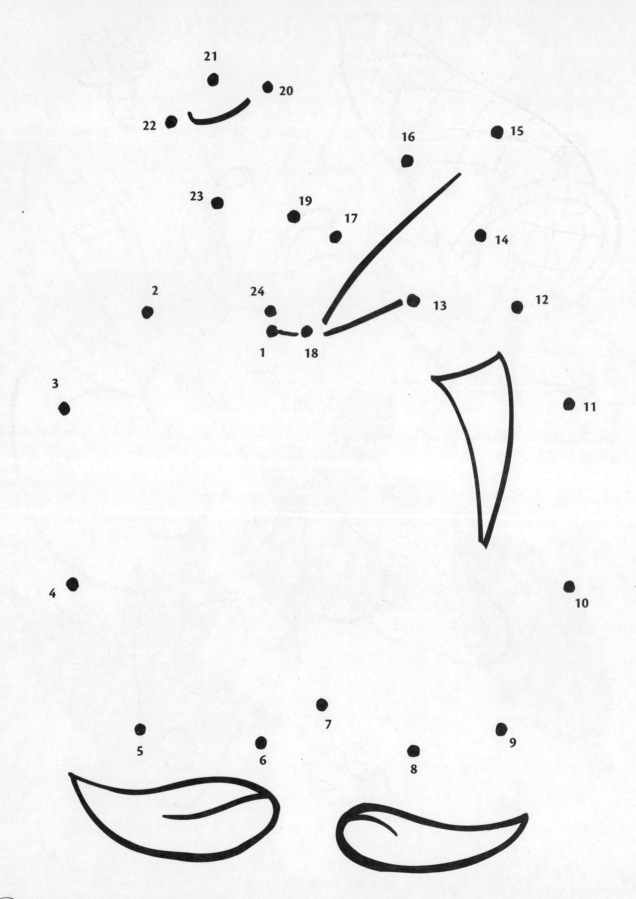

Find your way through the apple.

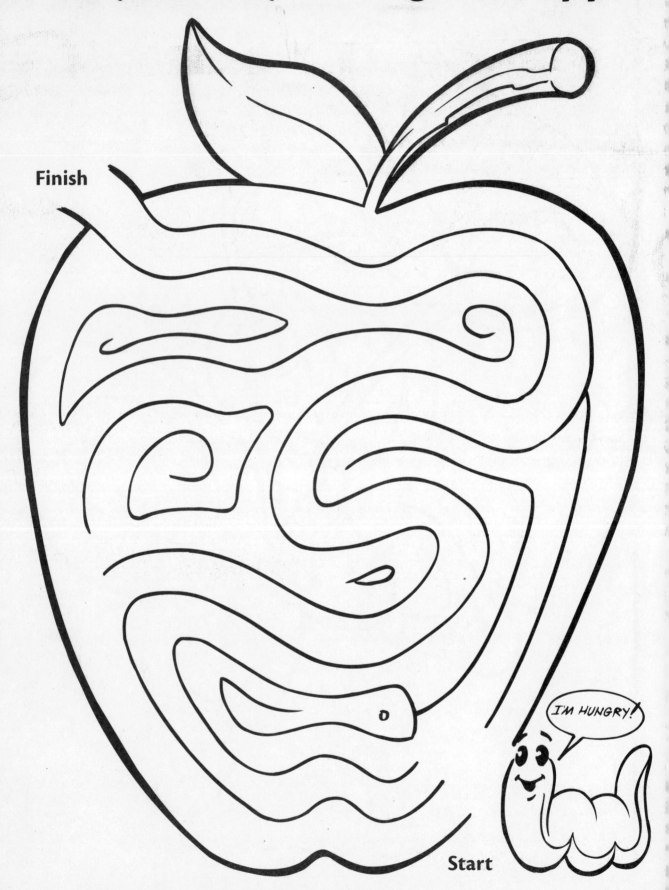

Which one does not belong?

A

B

C

D

Your Answer

289

Dalmatian Press

Crayola

USE YOUR IMAGINATION!

What is sitting in the flowers?

Draw a line from each bug to its matching shadow.

Answer: A-2; B-3; C-1

292

How many flowers do you count?

Your Answer

Dalmatian Press

Color by number.

1. Violet   2. Yellow   3. Lavender
4. Green   5. Red   6. Blue

Dalmatian Press

Finish drawing the happy frog.

USE YOUR IMAGINATION!

What is the little grasshopper dreaming about?

Trace and color!

304

Which one does not belong?

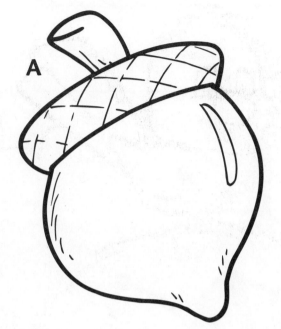

A

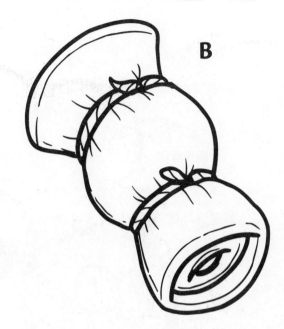

B

C

D

Your Answer

Answer: B

Connect the dots—and color!

Trace the line that leads from each flower pot.
Which one leads to the spade?

A   B   C

Your Answer

Answer: C

308

Draw a line from each shovel to its matching shape.

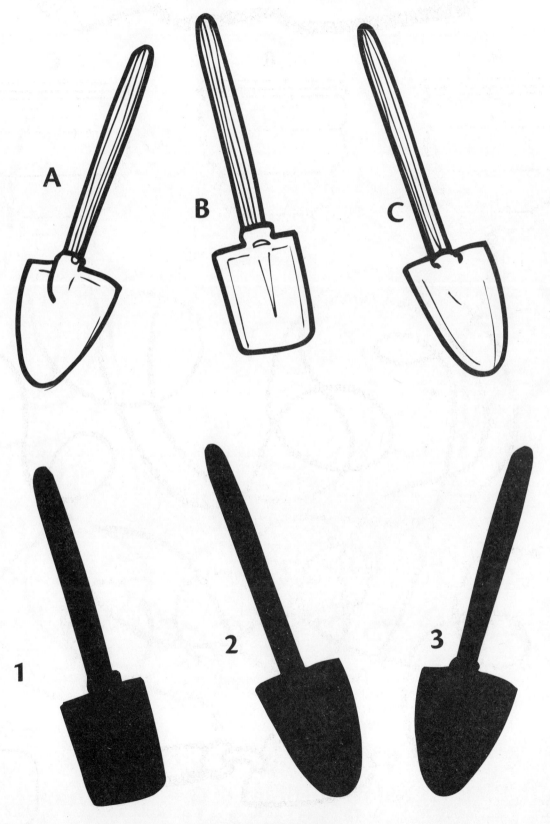

A

B

C

1

2

3

Dalmatian Press

Color by number.

1. Pink   2. Yellow   3. Blue   4. Green   5. Orange

Trace and color!

USE YOUR IMAGINATION!

Draw and color a picture of yourself playing ball with a doggy.

Color by number.

1. Green 2. Blue Green 3. Yellow
4. Orange 5. Red Orange 6. Blue

318

Bzzzz!